Someday

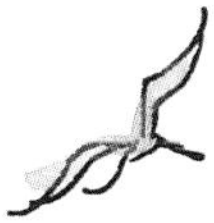

Someday

alison mcghee
peter h. reynolds

SCHOLASTIC INC.
New York Toronto London Auckland Sydney
Mexico City New Delhi Hong Kong Buenos Aires

One day I counted your fingers
and kissed each one.

One day the first snowflakes fell, and I held you up

and watched them melt on your baby skin.

One day
we crossed the street,
and you held my hand tight.

Then, you were my baby.

and now you are my child.

Sometimes, when you sleep, I watch you dream,

and I dream too....

That someday you will dive into the

Cool, clear water of a lake.

Someday
you will walk
into a deep wood.

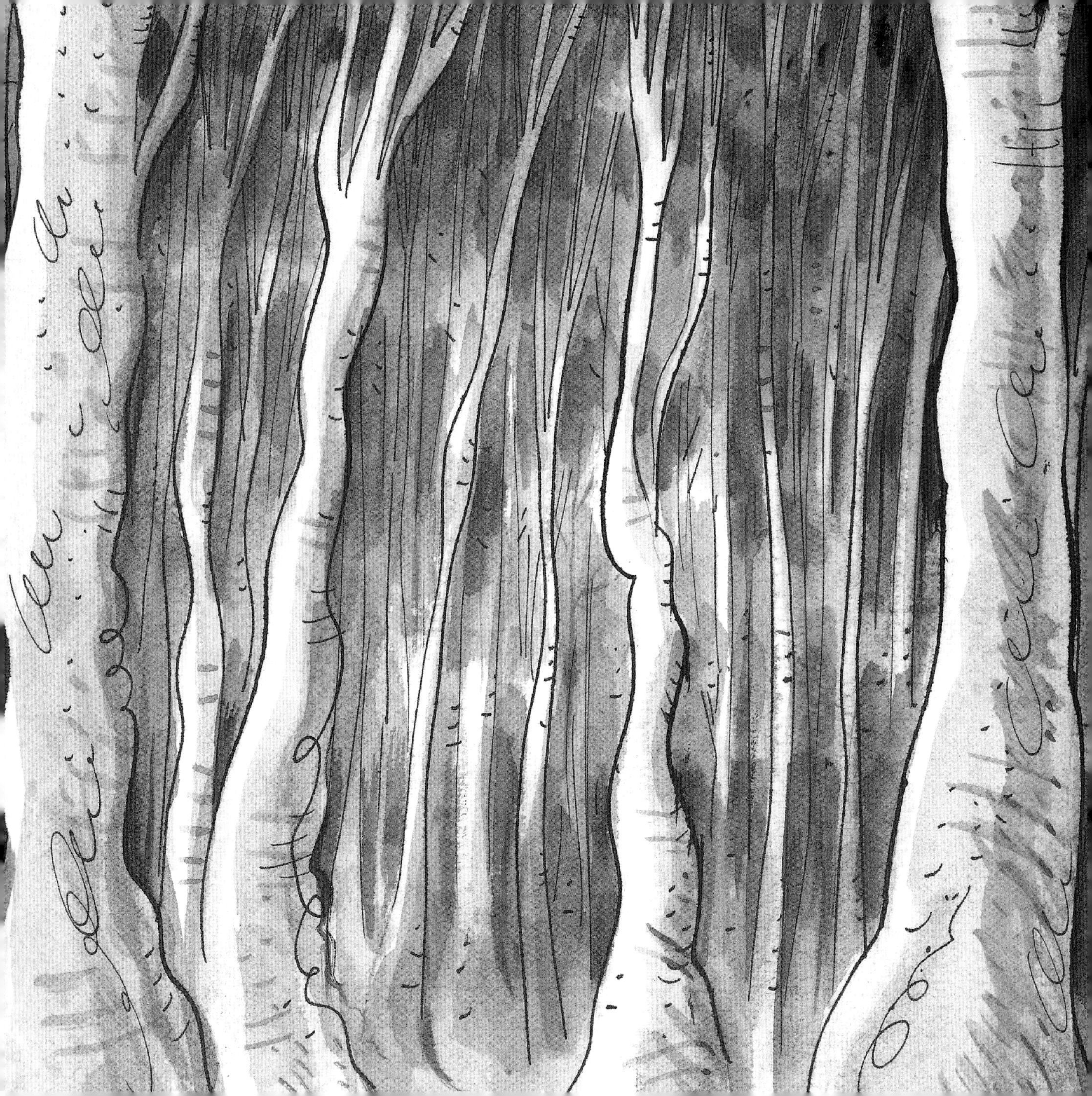

Someday your eyes

will be filled with a joy so deep that they shine.

Someday you

will run so fast and so far your heart will feel like fire.

Someday you will swing high—so high,

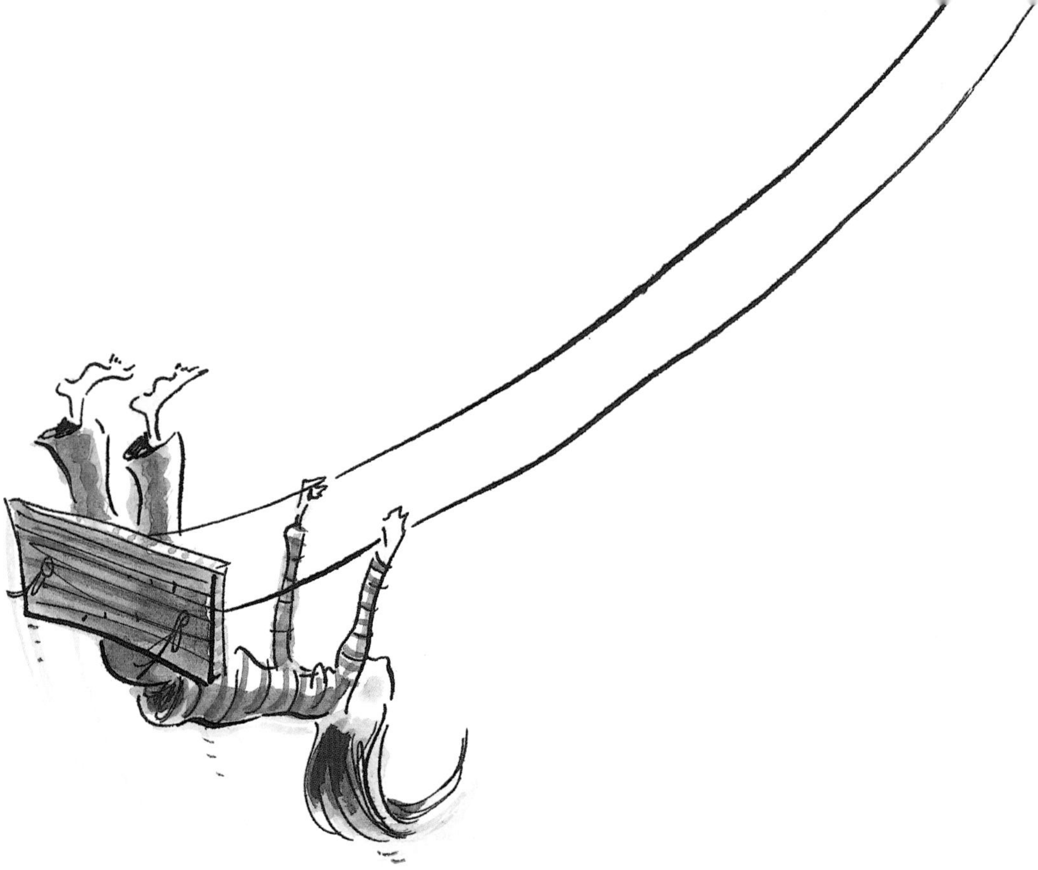

higher than you ever dared to swing.

Someday
you will hear something so sad
that you will fold up
with sorrow.

Someday you will call a song to the wind,

and the wind will carry your song away.

Someday I will stand on this porch

and watch your arms waving to me until I no longer see you.

Someday you will look at this house and

wonder how something that feels so big can look so small.

Someday you will feel
a small weight
against your strong back.

Someday I will
watch you brushing
your child's hair.

Someday, a long time
from now, your own hair will glow
silver in the sun.

And when that day comes, love,

you will remember me.

To Gabrielle Kirsch McGhee,
with love and respect
—A. M.

To the Queen Mother of our Family,
the very wise and beautiful
Hazel Gasson Reynolds
—P. H. R.

ISBN-13: 978-0-545-07611-1
ISBN-10: 0-545-07611-0

 Published by Scholastic Inc., 557 Broadway, New York, NY 10012, by arrangement with Atheneum Books for Young Readers, an imprint of Simon & Schuster Children's Publishing Division.

12 11 10 9 8 7 6 10 11 12 13/0

Printed in Singapore 46

First Scholastic printing, March 2008

Book design by Ann Bobco
The text of this book is handlettered by Peter H. Reynolds.
The illustrations for this book are rendered in pen and ink and watercolor.